The Star That Was

An Adoption Story

By Cheramy Hassen

Illustrated by Sergio Drumond

To my amazing children--Coleman, Caitlin, Sora and Chase who each arrived in their own miraculous way.

The stars were twinkling in the midnight sky. I searched the heavens though I wasn't sure why.

My arms felt empty and then I knew my heart was looking for the star that was you!

I wasn't sure how I'd find you but surely you knew, I'd never stop looking until then we were two.

Someday I knew I would call you my own, dreaming of the day you would finally come home.

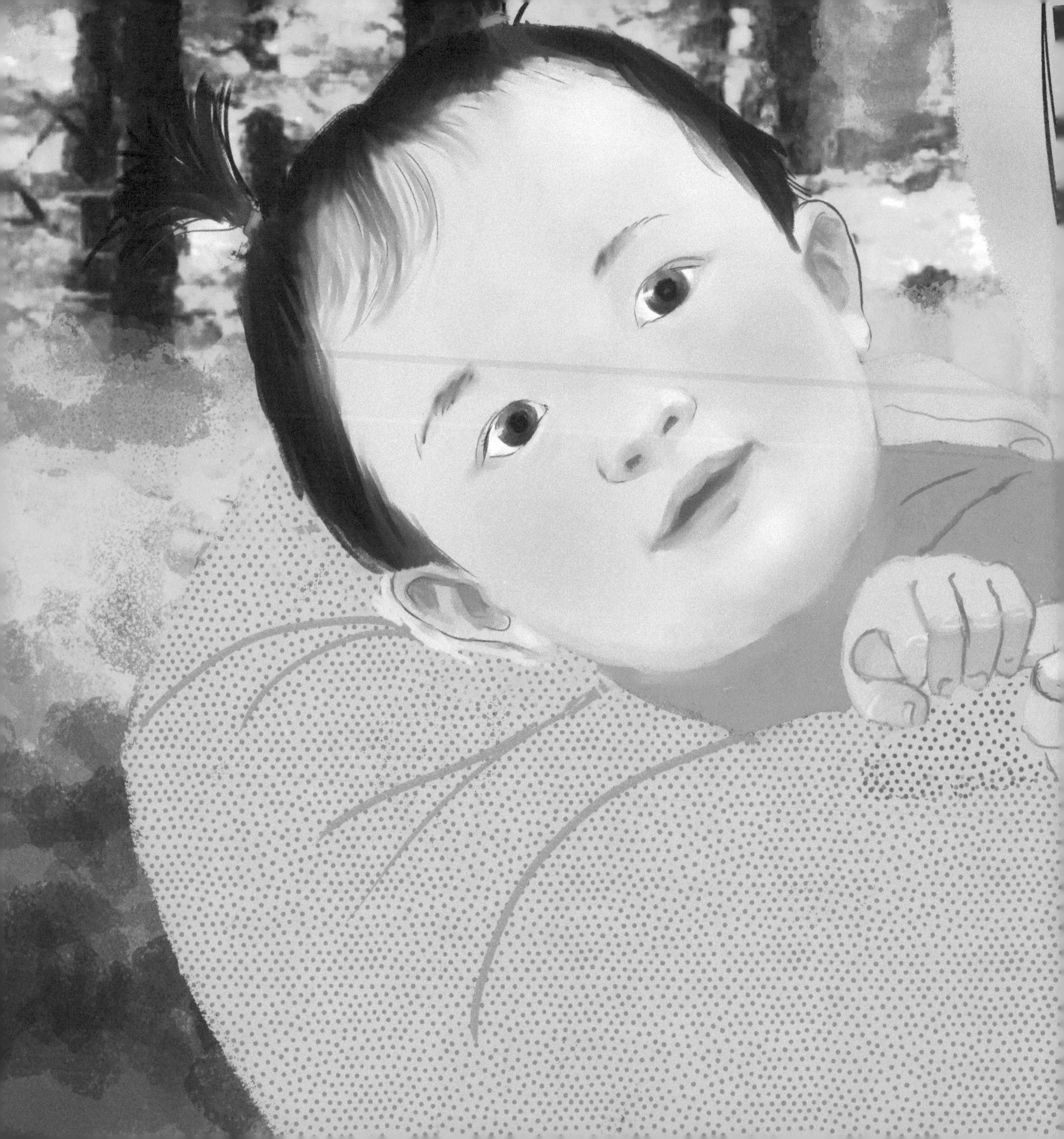

Another mother first held your hand while dreaming of the life she hoped you would have.

The day that I met you I snuggled you close feeling so blessed I was the mother she chose.

That night the stars were twinkling as the angels started singing, from the beginning of time God knew you were mine.

As an adoption social worker, Cheramy Hassen has had a part in bringing all kinds of families together for over 35 years. She herself is an adoptive mother who knows first hand the miracle of adoption. A mother of four and grandmother of five she lives in Washington State with her husband Rick.

CPSIA information can be obtained
at www.ICGtesting.com
Printed in the USA
LVHW070958300123
738064LV00009B/57

* 9 7 8 1 9 5 1 8 0 6 4 8 4 *